BIG IDEA'S
Jonah
a VeggieTales Movie™

SPECIAL COLLECTOR'S EDITION

written by Cindy Kenney

Based on the Movie: Jonah – a VeggieTales Movie
Written and Directed by Phil Vischer and Mike Nawrocki

BIG IDEA
BOOKS™

Zonderkidz

www.bigidea.com

Zonder**kidz**™
The children's group of Zondervan
www.zonderkidz.com

Special Collector's Edition of Big Idea's Jonah – a VeggieTales Movie
ISBN: 0-310-70462-6
Copyright © 2002 by Big Idea Productions, Inc.

Requests for information should be addressed to:
Zonderkidz, Grand Rapids, Michigan 49530

Written by: Cindy Kenney
Editor: Phil Vischer and Gwen Ellis
Cover and Interior Design: John Trent
Art Direction: Karen Poth

Printed in Mexico
02 03 04 05/RRD/5 4 3 2 1

For Phil and Mike and everyone at Big Idea
who worked so hard to make this happen.

COVER IMAGE: Still frame of Jonah and Reginald overlooking Nineveh. Background painting by Chuck Vollmer.

FOLLOWING PAGE: Color key of outside the Joppa marketplace by Brad Hicks.

CONTENTS

FOREWORD BY PHIL VISCHER 7

WHAT'S THE BIG IDEA? 8

WHY VEGETABLES? 10

ENTER...THE TOMATO 11

IT ALL STARTS WITH A NUGGET 13

WHAT ABOUT SILLY SONGS? 14

"MY HUSBAND AND I ARE CRACKING UP TOO!" 16

WHY JONAH? 18

THE TEAM 22

THE MISSION 25

JONAH 27

THE BIG FISH 29

KHALIL 30

THE PIRATES WHO DON'T DO ANYTHING 31

BOB, DAD, JUNIOR, AND FRIENDS 32

REGINALD AND TWIPPO 33

JONAH'S VISUAL JOURNEY 35

THE SEAFOOD RESTAURANT 36

JOPPA AND NINEVEH 37

THE SHIP 40

INSIDE THE WHALE 45

THE STORY: JONAH'S JOURNEY COMES TO LIFE! 49

MUSIC, SOUND, AND SPECIAL EFFECTS 52

FROM BIG IDEA TO YOU! 54

JONAH STORYBOOK 57

Movies. We love 'em! As a young boy, I had the privilege of taking my father to his first movie in a theater. (He grew up in a family where theaters were off limits.) It was Disney's live-action classic, "The Apple Dumpling Gang." We all laughed our heads off as Tim Conway and Don Knotts bumbled their way through this comic western and came home with a shared memory that made us inexplicably closer as a family. A few years later we actually took my father's parents—my grandparents—to their first (and only) film in a theater: The Jesus Film. My grandfather fell asleep before it was over. (He'd read the book, so he knew how it ended.)

My childhood was filled with memorable experiences at the movies. But it wasn't until a little film called "Star Wars" that I realized the full potential of this medium, and I was smitten. Much of what I have attempted to do since the age of eight has led up to the contents of this book, and Big Idea's first real movie, Jonah. As excited as I am about the film and its powerful message of compassion and mercy, I'm even more excited about what it represents. Big Idea is in the film business!

So why should you care? With 10-12 animated films hitting American theaters every year, do we really need more? Absolutely! Because unlike most film studios, Big Idea isn't in this business for the "art" or the money. We don't make films to impress our friends or to win the praise of film critics and fans. We make films to make the world a better place. We try as best we can to promote healthy relationships between friends, families, and ultimately between everyone and the God who "made them special and loves them very much." And **that** kind of film studio is in very short supply!

I hope you enjoy this peek behind the scenes at Big Idea, as well as the story within that so many artists have worked so hard crafting. It is a privilege to work with Big Idea's talented artists—artists who have left some of the world's finest studios, moving their families across the country to Chicago just for the chance to see their gifts used to bring biblical values and lessons to families everywhere. Jonah would not have been possible without the contributions of far too many people to mention here.

As I write this foreword, we still have a few more months of production on Jonah ahead of us, but I'm already looking forward to bringing my grandfather to his **second** movie in a theater. And if we've done our jobs well, he might actually stay awake till the end!

Phil Vischer

WHAT'S THE BIG IDEA?

In 1966 a normal, average boy was born on a normal, average day in Muscatine, Iowa. It was a small town on the banks of the Mississippi River. He was a quiet boy, but the silly things that kept popping into his head managed to get him in trouble in Sunday school all the same. His name was Phil Vischer.

His first-grade teacher noticed Phil loved to draw, so she put him to work decorating bulletin boards. By the age of eight he had borrowed his grandfather's Super 8 movie camera and was making his own short animated films. From puppets to Legos, to GI Joes and washcloths, Phil Vischer found he loved bringing things to life. His grandfather didn't get his camera back until Phil headed off to college. By then it didn't work anymore.

Even before heading off to college, Phil noticed that he really liked movies and TV shows. But he also noticed that the values that came from those TV stories didn't seem to line up well with the values he had learned in Sunday school. In fact, sometimes they seemed to be the exact opposite! He also noticed that many of the shows that were really fun to watch weren't very good for you. And many of the shows that were good for you weren't much fun to watch. Phil thought that maybe someone should do something about this problem.

At St. Paul Bible College in chilly Minnesota, Phil tried out for the puppet team and met a really tall kid from Denver named Mike Nawrocki. Though no one knew it at the time, Bob the Tomato had just met Larry the Cucumber. After a few years of Bible college, Mike moved to Chicago with Phil. Mike was going to be a doctor. Phil was going to make movies. Within a few months, they both found themselves working at a video production house, making training videos to help truck drivers and department store salesmen. It was a way to make a living, but neither Phil nor Mike had come anywhere close to accomplishing their goals. Phil knew he definitely wasn't changing the world, and Mike still wanted to be a doctor.

Three years later, Phil and Mike—with the help of several friends—were creating *Where's God When I'm S-Scared?*, the first episode of the first fully 3D computer-animated video series in America. *VeggieTales* was born. Suddenly, Phil was pretty sure he could see how God wanted him to change the world. And Mike was pretty sure God didn't want him to be a doctor. He wanted him to be a cucumber.

Those three years are a pretty amazing story...but that will have to wait for another book!

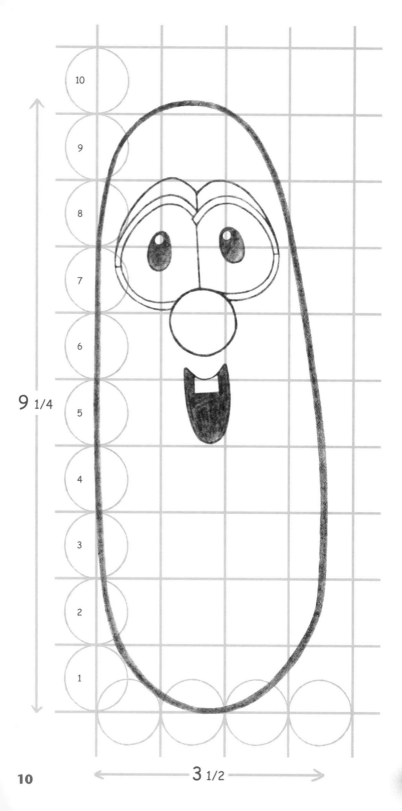

10

9 1/4

3 1/2

Phil started playing around with ideas for a show of his own way back in 1991. Some people have speculated that Phil chose vegetables because he wanted kids to eat more vegetables. Some have suggested that he must have wanted kids to eat *fewer* vegetables. ("I can't eat it! It's *Bob*!") Others have simply assumed he was just a kid who really, really *loved* his vegetables. None of the above is correct. The real answer is neither dietary nor creative, but technical. In 1991, computer animation software couldn't create hair, fur, or clothes; and was having a pretty hard time with arms and legs. Most animators were waiting for the software to develop further before trying to create long films with computer-generated characters. But Phil didn't want to wait. So he decided he would have to come up with characters that were bald, limbless, and naked.

His first idea was a candy bar. *That could work*, he thought. Phil built a little candy bar on the computer and tacked on some big, goofy eyes. He was rather pleased—until his wife, Lisa, walked through the room and noted that moms wouldn't be very happy if Phil made their kids fall in love with candy bars. Good point! Okay, he concurred. Then what *wouldn't* moms mind their kids falling in love with? The next thing that popped into Phil's head was a cucumber. What's not to like about cucumbers? Phil quickly whipped up a cucumber on the computer, pulled the eyes off the candy bar and stuck them on (changing them from brown to green), then added a goofy little grin and one big tooth. Bingo! A star was born!

Larry was the first veggie character. Phil called him "Mr. Cuke" and put him through his paces in a twelve-second scene. It worked! He moved, he smiled, and he communicated with the viewer. But he was alone, and it was not good. Since Mr. Cuke was tall and thin, Phil thought his partner should be short and round. And, well, since red and green are complimentary colors, the choice was obvious! "Mr. Cuke" got a short, round, red sidekick, and Bob and Larry—the Abbott and Costello of the vegetable world—came to be.

Phil and Mike worked for a few weeks, producing a two-minute film to test out the new duo, with Mike providing the voice for the cucumber and Phil voicing the tomato. Even in this very first film (produced in 1992), Phil and Mike's personalities shone through as Bob gave an impassioned speech on behalf of a new kids' show called *VeggieTales*. It was a show with the potential to "change the world!" Meanwhile, Larry hopped around behind Bob, looking for his blue, plastic, wind-up lobster.

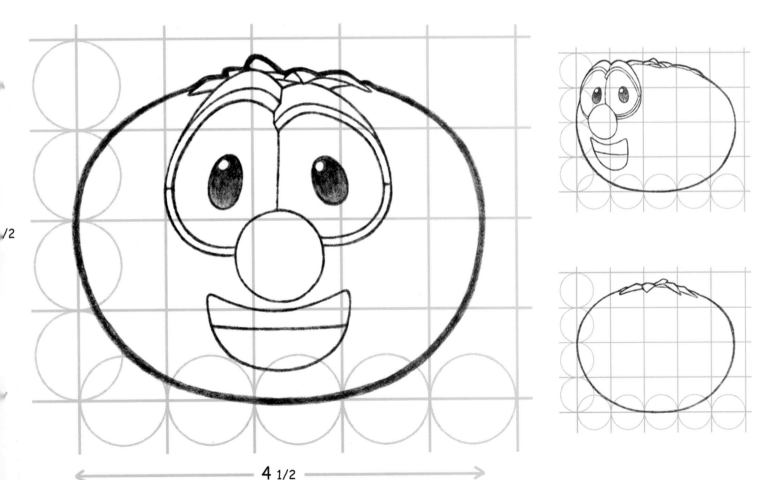

/2

4 1/2

ABOVE: Early concept of Jonah in the
whale by Joseph Sapulich.

Some look for chicken...others for gold. But at Big Idea, every story starts with a "nugget of truth"—a lesson or value from the Bible so clear and simple, even a four-year-old can pick it up and carry it around for the rest of his or her life. The next challenge was putting a story together. The heart and soul of each one of those stories usually comes from Phil or Mike. "Every show we do starts with a nugget of truth," explains Phil. That's how stories about loving our neighbors, standing up for what we believe in, or little guys doing big things with God's help come into existence. Starting with a nugget on a single piece of paper, Phil, Mike, and the other Big Idea writers and story artists proceed to build a script.

But the challenge doesn't stop there. The folks at Big Idea fill each story with enough music, drama, and humor to be sure it will appeal to *everyone* in the family, not just little kids. And that's not always easy, especially when you're working with characters who don't have any arms or legs!

Telling stories through the medium of animation requires a massive amount of leadership and teamwork. Not only do Phil and Mike have to communicate a story through a carefully woven script, but that script must then become the means by which the entire studio can capture their vision. And while a team of only four people completed the first *VeggieTales* film, on a visit to Big Idea's studios today, you will find more than two hundred people toiling away!

The next step for Phil and Mike is to work with the producer, story artists, animators, and songwriters to create visual imagery and music that will bring life to the story they want to tell. Great care is taken with the actual words used so that the characters don't say what could be better shown on the screen. Follow that up by carefully designing and building the "sets" (in the computer, of course). Complete the process by animating the characters and then adding light, music, and sound effects to affect the overall mood and tone of the film.

Each step of the way, the director must pay particular attention to how the audience will follow the story. He has to ask himself questions like: *Will they understand this part? Am I boring them? Will this make them laugh? Is that scene too scary for the kids?* And, most importantly, they have to ask: *Have we successfully communicated the biblical lesson we began with?* From the time a thirty-minute *VeggieTales* story is conceived, it may be eighteen months before it appears in stores. For Big Idea's first theatrical film, *Jonah*, the production spanned more than two-and-a-half years!

Despite the complexity of making an animated film, the results are rewarding. Not only do Phil, Mike, and their team get to enjoy the fruits of their labor, but it becomes an experience that can be shared with many. Big Idea has an opportunity to reach out to people everywhere with messages that families can trust. "Sunday Morning Values, Saturday Morning Fun." That's pretty much what Phil has been pursuing since he was eight!

Most of Larry's famous "Silly Songs" come from Larry's alter ego, Mike Nawrocki. But ask Mike how he comes up with such zaniness, and he'll just shrug. Sometimes the songs hit him while he's driving. "The Song of the Cebú" started hatching while Mike was traveling in Columbia with his wife. After seeing several "Cebús" (a type of cow) walking down a street together, the song came to life. Then there was the morning he got out of the shower and couldn't find his razor. "Oh, where...is my razor?" he started singing. A few hours later, he was in Phil's office singing his next idea for a silly song! After Phil pointed out that they probably didn't want kids running around their houses looking for razors, Mike rethought his idea. Within minutes, "The Hairbrush Song" was born!

Working with Big Idea music director, Kurt Heinecke, Phil and Mike have enjoyed putting together lots of Silly Songs for *VeggieTales* fans over the years. Recently, fans had the opportunity to vote for their favorites in "The Ultimate Silly Song Countdown," a collection of the top ten silliest Silly Songs hosted by The Pirates Who Don't Do Anything! "Oh, Where Is My Hairbrush?" was the winner!

When the first copies of "Where's God When I'm Scared?" started getting passed around in 1993, Phil was thrilled to hear that kids really liked it. Then he got a letter from a couple in Iowa who decorated Bob and Larry pumpkins for Halloween. The strange thing: the couple didn't have any kids. Then a woman from Texas sent Big Idea an invitation she had made to a *VeggieTales* party. "What's so weird about that?" you ask. It was a party for single adults, and no kids were invited. Over the years the letters have poured in...*VeggieTales* parties on college campuses...entire churches watching *VeggieTales* together...pastors delivering sermons wearing *VeggieTales* ties...Larry the Cucumber T-shirts popping up in dance clubs in downtown Chicago. So what gives?

Phil and Mike had managed to create a show that seemed to appeal to *everyone*, not just kids. From the very beginning, Phil and Mike weren't simply interested in creating films that kids would find amusing; they wanted to make films that *they* would find amusing too. It just turns out that the things Phil and Mike find funny, a lot of other people find funny too!

This provided a tremendous benefit to audiences of all ages. With some kids' videos, a parent is likely to put in the tape, press play, then make a mad dash to get out of the room. That's because there's really nothing in the video that appeals to anyone over the age of four. The problem with this dynamic is that even if the show has good lessons to teach, the parents will never hear them and thus won't be able to help their kids apply them in the future. By creating a show like *VeggieTales*, entire families are watching the films together and the parents and older kids are learning and applying the lessons right alongside the little tykes!

Because of this unique mix of "Sunday Morning Values" and "Saturday Morning Fun," Big Idea receives more than sixty thousand letters, cards, and E-mails every year from parents and fans who want to say thanks. People all around the country have been looking for a great way for families to be reminded of the simple truths found in the Bible! Reading those messages gives the artists at Big Idea the added motivation to keep on working—even when their hours are long, their computers crash, and the last thing in the world they want to look at is another vegetable!

Ever since Phil Vischer was a little boy, he wanted to make movies. Making the half-hour *VeggieTales* home videos has been fun, but Phil has always looked forward to the day he could give families a *VeggieTales* story for the BIG screen!

When Big Idea decided they were ready to create their first full-length animated feature film, they needed a really great idea and a really BIG story! They needed the kind of story that would make people say, "Oh, I can't wait to see that!" And the story of the biblical character Jonah was one of the first that came to their minds.

At first, *Jonah* was going to be a special forty-five-minute *VeggieTales* video. But when Mike Nawrocki started writing the script and at page 17 still hadn't gotten to the actual story of Jonah, Phil and Mike decided, "Hey! Maybe this is something more!" They also discovered that the biblical story of Jonah involves a much larger lesson than is usually represented in the average Sunday school or storybook version.

Hence, *Jonah – a VeggieTales Movie* was born! It's a story told within the context of another story—sort of like the movie *Titanic*. Phil and Mike wanted to do a historical recreation of the epic biblical account, but they also wanted the audience to view the story as relevant to their own lives. By setting it in the framework of contemporary life, this helps an audience see how the ancient story affects them today.

TOP: Early concept of Jonah in the belly of the whale by Joseph Sapulich.

BOTTOM: Still frame of Jonah and Reginald. Background painting by Chuck Vollmer.

Telling a story in this context is the perfect way to relate the tale of Jonah — a Bible story with a very unusual ending. Even though most Sunday school retellings of the story focus on obedience and end with Jonah happily heading off to Nineveh to present the Ninevites with God's message, Phil and Mike wanted to tell the *whole* story. And the whole story ends with a *very* grumpy prophet sitting next to a worm-chewed weed cursing the day he was born because God had the audacity to forgive Israel's archenemies!

Phil and Mike quickly concluded that the story isn't really about obedience at all; it is about compassion and mercy. They also concluded that the final scene of Jonah whimpering in the sun because a worm killed his weed just *had* to be in the film. But of course, ending the entire film on this pathetic note, while being biblically accurate, might not be that much fun for a theater full of people.

To solve this quandary, the story begins in a present-day setting as Bob the Tomato, Dad Asparagus, and a van full of veggie kids are dealing with several dilemmas. Solving those dilemmas requires two biblical values—compassion and mercy. After a wild run-in with an angry mother porcupine, our travelers find themselves in an old seafood restaurant, face-to-face with everyone's favorite motivationally-challenged seafarers, The Pirates Who Don't Do Anything. The pirates overhear the travelers' conversations and offer to tell them a little story that might do them some good!

TOP: Visual development of van on winding road by Joseph Sapulich.

BOTTOM: Visual development of Captain Pa on ship by Joseph Sapulich.

So the pirates take everyone on a journey back in time— a journey that Jonah traveled in approximately 785 B.C. That journey in the movie ends when Jonah is asked the question, "Did you ever think that maybe God wants to give *everyone* a second chance?" Because the biblical account of Jonah doesn't end clearly, the movie version of Jonah shows how that question is played out in the contemporary framework. This challenges the audience with how *they* should react as a result of knowing what the Bible says about compassion and mercy. By staying true to the Bible, but wrapping up the story in a really clever way in the "real" world, Big Idea's retelling of *Jonah* proves to be a very unique, *very* entertaining movie!

OPPOSITE: Color key of Joppa Harbor by Brad Hicks, designed by Joseph Sapulich.

TOP: Color key of the road to Nineveh by Brad Hicks.

CENTER: Background painting of Nineveh by Chuck Vollmer.

BOTTOM: Color key of Twippo's big musical number by Brad Hicks.

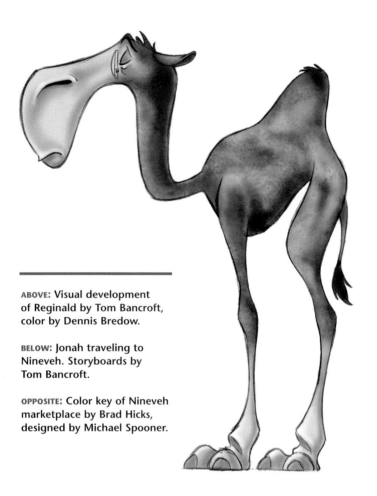

ABOVE: Visual development of Reginald by Tom Bancroft, color by Dennis Bredow.

BELOW: Jonah traveling to Nineveh. Storyboards by Tom Bancroft.

OPPOSITE: Color key of Nineveh marketplace by Brad Hicks, designed by Michael Spooner.

Jonah–a *VeggieTales Movie* started with just an idea. But now the idea is exploding into a commitment that takes a huge team to complete. And that's nothing to sneeze at, particularly in a world that has come to demand big things when the curtain goes up. Big Idea has grown its team from only ten back in 1995 to more than two hundred. They've added people like Michael Spooner, Tim Hodge, Tom Bancroft and Chuck Vollmer from Disney Feature Animation—artists who worked on films like *Mulan* and *The Lion King*. They also have Dan Philips and the husband and wife team, Ameake and Tom Owens from Dreamworks Feature Animation—who have worked on films like *The Road To Eldorado* and *The Prince of Egypt*. Their experience, combined with the rest of the Big Idea team, has helped to create a big screen adventure that takes "Sunday Morning Values, Saturday Morning Fun" to a whole new level!

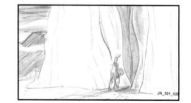

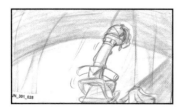

So why have these tremendously gifted artists moved their families from all over the country to work in a former Woolworth's store located inside a mall in the suburbs of Chicago? Because they, like Phil, want to change the world. Because they want to see their gifts used to do more than make money for giant media companies or sell fast-food kids' meals. They want to tell stories that will make a parent's job *easier*, not harder. They want to be a part of the solution, not the problem. This desire to use their skills to spread biblical values throughout our culture has built a truly extraordinary team in a mall in the suburbs of Chicago. The world may never be the same!

OPPOSITE: Veggies entering the restaurant. Storyboards by Tim Hodge.

LEFT: Color key of the restaurant lobby by Brad Hicks, designed by Joseph Sapulich.

TOP: Color key of the restaurant dining area by Brad Hicks.

Even the greatest story line won't come to life if it isn't filled with good characters. To meet this challenge, over the years Big Idea has developed an entire cornucopia of vegetables, and people love them. Naturally, Big Idea went to those endearing stars to create their first movie, but they also added a couple of new ones, just for fun. The result is more than a tossed salad...it is magical!

Who would get the lead role in this biblical epic? After auditions were over, Archibald Asparagus won everyone over, hands down... well... so to speak. Archibald is Big Idea's proper English gentleman (based loosely on Monty Python's John Cleese) who wants everything to be "just right." But that's hardly what happens in the story of Jonah, which made Archibald the obvious choice. This tall, somewhat stuffy asparagus is guaranteed to make audiences laugh. Mike Nawrocki adds, "He also looks so smashing in khaki!"

Jonah was a prophet, and prophets were the people that God chose to do the very special job of delivering his messages to Israel. As Pa Grape tells us in the story, "They were a little like mailmen, except *their* letters came *straight from God!*" Jonah the prophet gets a whopper of a message that teaches everyone a lot about compassion, mercy, and second chances.

TOP RIGHT: Early concept of Jonah in ship's hold by Joseph Sapulich.

BOTTOM RIGHT: Visual development of Jonah and Reginald in the desert by Joseph Sapulich.

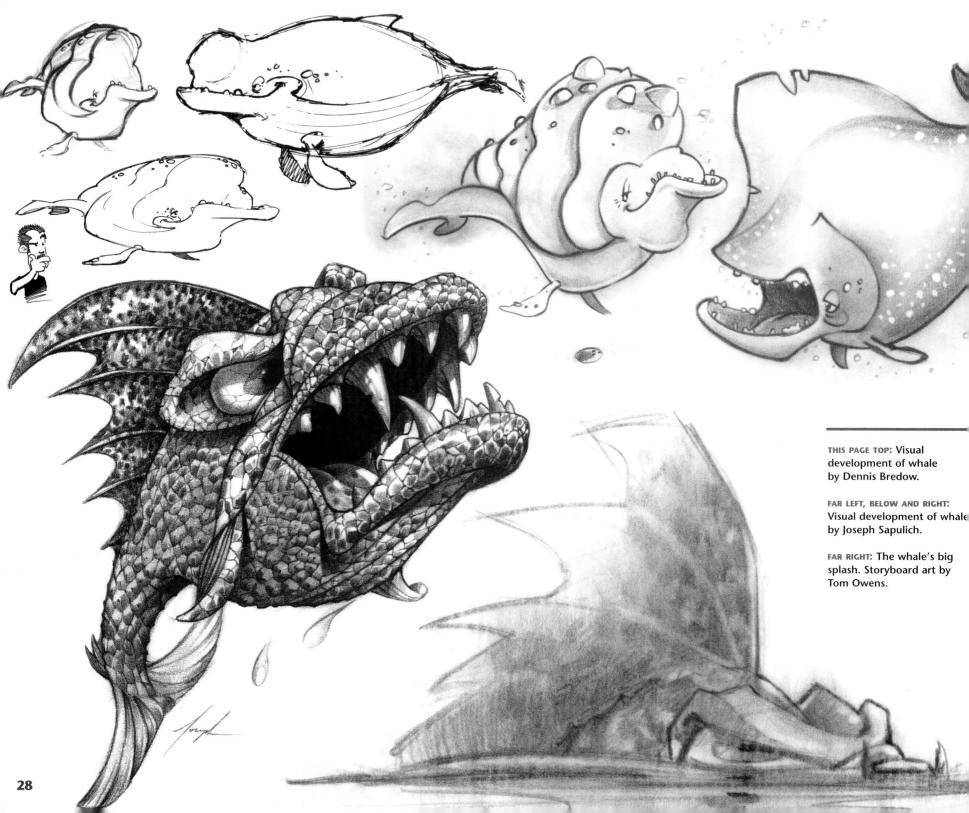

THIS PAGE TOP: Visual development of whale by Dennis Bredow.

FAR LEFT, BELOW AND RIGHT: Visual development of whale by Joseph Sapulich.

FAR RIGHT: The whale's big splash. Storyboard art by Tom Owens.

28

The story of Jonah is all about a prophet who knew just what God wanted him to do but did the exact opposite, causing him to end up in one of the stickiest situations ever—the belly of a whale (or "great fish," depending on your translation). The extraordinary character of the big sea creature went through many transformations during his Bible creation. He started out quite frightening! But when everything was said and done, Tim Hodge, Head of Story Development, explained, "The trick was to make the whale terrifying to the characters in the film, but at the same time make the audience laugh until they wet their pants. If I can make Jonah scream with terror and a kid scream with laughter at the same time, then I've done my job well."

Some biblical scholars believe that the big fish was most likely a sperm whale or a whale shark. These great fish were known to gulp down grown men who were actually found alive inside the stomach of these fish later on.

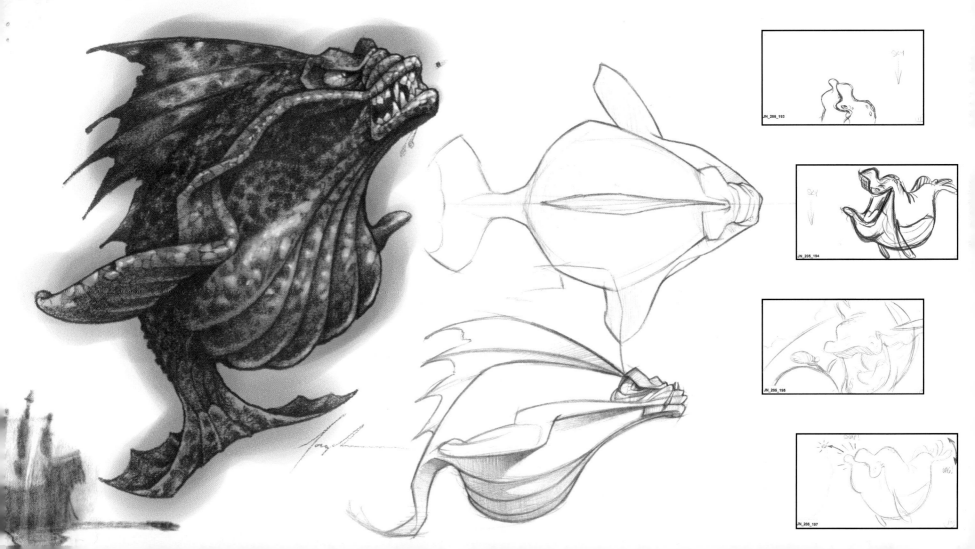

Khalil is a caterpillar. Well, actually, that's only half true. His mother was a caterpillar; his father was a worm. But he's "okay with that now." At least that's what he tells us in the movie. *Khalil* is pronounced Kah-leel and is an Arabic word that means "friendly." The look of this new character was inspired by Big Idea storyboard artist, Luis Contreras. When it came to finding a voice for this character, Big Idea looked all over the United States, Canada and even London. Little did they know that Khalil's unique voice was right there at Big Idea! Head of Story, Tim Hodge, makes the voice of Khalil come to life.

This middle-eastern wormapillar comes from a family in which various talents, habits, and traits "run very deeply." But when it comes to patience with Jonah's stubbornness, he finally admits even *he* has his limits.

THIS PAGE: Visual development of Khalil by Tom Bancroft, Everett Downing and Daniel López Muñoz, color by Dennis Bredow.

LEFT: Early concept of the pirates by Daniel López Muñoz.

ABOVE: The pirates begin to tell the story of Jonah. Storyboard art by Luis Contreras.

BELOW: Color concept of the pirates by Joseph Sapulich.

These lazy pirates (played by Larry the Cucumber, Pa Grape, and everyone's favorite decorative gourd, Mr. Lunt) first appeared in their own Silly Song on the first *VeggieTales* sing-along video, "A Very Silly Sing-along." Immediately enjoyed by audiences of all ages, they were back by popular demand as the hosts of "The Ultimate Silly Song Countdown." Because Jonah needs a crew desperate enough to attempt the harrowing journey from Joppa to Tarshish—literally the other end of the known world at the time—they were just the right pirates for the job! Especially when Jonah tells them "money is no object," filling their heads with visions of limitless cheese curls and root beer!

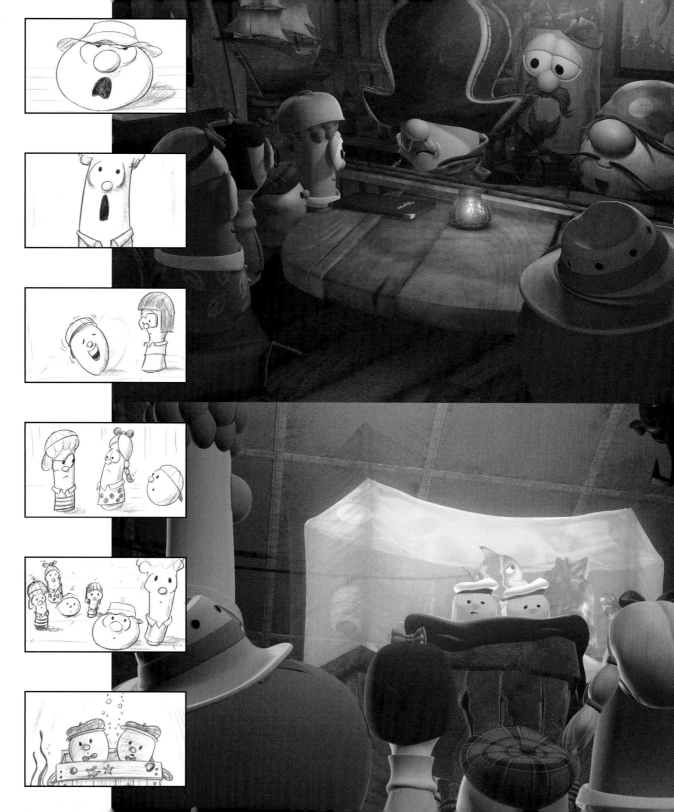

The contemporary story that frames the biblical epic needed everyday characters with whom folks of all ages could identify. What better veggies than Bob the Tomato, Dad Asparagus, his son Junior, and their friends Laura, Annie, and Percy? Together, they set the framework for a dilemma to which everyone can relate.

The French Peas, Jean-Claude and Phillipe, first came to life in "Dave and the Giant Pickle." These aggravating peas were hilariously inspired by the Frenchmen in the classic Monty Python film, "The Holy Grail." A huge hit, the French Peas returned to taunt the Israelites from the walls of Jericho in "Josh and the Big Wall," as well as numerous other cameos in various *VeggieTales* videos. In *Jonah*, they appear in dual roles—first as the seafood restaurant maître d's in the contemporary scenes and then again as fish-slappers in Nineveh.

TOP: The pirates tell the story of Jonah. Production still.

INSET: The commotion is interrupted by the maître d'. Storyboard art by Luis Contreras.

BOTTOM: The French Peas welcome the gang into the eerie restaurant. Production still.

Because there were no cars back in Bible-times, prophets like Jonah were known to travel by foot or camel. Although a trusted friend and loyal companion to this prophet, even Reginald the camel hits the road at the end of the story when Jonah doesn't seem to learn his lesson.

Back by popular demand? Archibald himself returns at the end of the story in a brand-new role, this time as the greatly anticipated concert star, Twippo. The singer of children's songs Raffi mixed with a little Elvis inspired the character of Twippo.

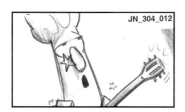

TOP RIGHT: Turnarounds and rough facial expressions of Reginald by Tom Bancroft.

ABOVE AND RIGHT: Twippo performs the big finale. Storyboard art by Luis Contreras. Color key by Brad Hicks, designed by Joseph Sapulich.

Computer animation brings a story to life through a mix of traditional artistry and mind-blowing technology. Jonah's animated journey began with research, imagination, and a whole lot of drawing!

Michael Spooner, Head of Visual Development, and Joseph Sapulich, Art Director for *Jonah*, were responsible for the movie's overall look. It was their job to create the images that would provide the design direction for the story's many settings.

Jonah – a VeggieTales Movie actually required two different looks. One look was the contemporary, modern-day feel of the traveling veggies as they adventure through the woods and wind up in the mysterious seafood restaurant. But secondly, Michael and Joe had to create the look of the biblical epic itself. This look had to capture a realistic re-reation of a biblical era and also accommodate bouncing, talking vegetables.

LEFT: Jonah traveling to Nineveh. Visual development by Joseph Sapulich.

TOP RIGHT: Color key of the restaurant dining room by Brad Hicks.

BOTTOM RIGHT: Color key of Joppa by Brad Hicks.

The seafood restaurant has an abandoned, eerie, *Twilight Zone* look and feel. To capture the atmosphere accurately, the directors and artists spent hours visiting a variety of seafood restaurants. Tim Hodge admits, "This was especially difficult because I don't care for seafood, and it's kind of embarrassing to go into these restaurants and always order a cheeseburger."

TOP: Color key of the restaurant exterior by Brad Hicks, designed by Joseph Sapulich.

ABOVE: The gang discovers the eerie seafood restaurant. Storyboard art by Tim Hodge.

RIGHT: Color key of the restaurant lobby by Brad Hicks.

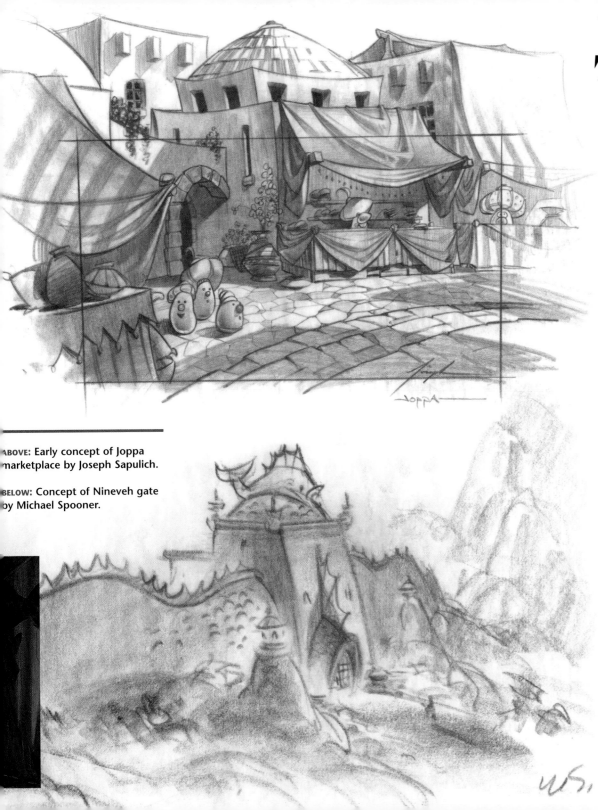

ABOVE: Early concept of Joppa marketplace by Joseph Sapulich.

BELOW: Concept of Nineveh gate by Michael Spooner.

The start of Jonah's historical journey begins in Joppa, where Jonah first receives the message from God that he should go to Nineveh and tell the people to stop being mean. The folks at Big Idea were going to travel to Joppa to get a feel for what it was like there, but then they realized it's probably changed a little over the last three thousand years...so they did their research right in Illinois.

Big Idea artists Joseph Sapulich and Dennis Bredow designed Joppa, while Michael Spooner, Daniel López Muñoz and Joseph Sapulich created Nineveh. Having separate artists work on the contrasting sites provided each location with a unique look and style.

Joe's design for Joppa needed to suggest a place filled with kind people who were always interested in hearing a new message from God. To capture this look, Joe fashioned a city built on a Mediterranean seacoast, then added round, happy buildings with puffy, almost "frosting-like," decorations. These "poofs," as they came to be called, found their way onto the tents, merchants' booths, even the "Joppa-nians" hats!

The design of Nineveh, on the other hand, had to reflect a city that didn't know right from wrong, had never heard the Word of God, and had a history of being mean and cruel toward Israel. Excavation has actually shown that the Ninevites worshiped a fish god, "Dagon," and some biblical scholars believe that is why they listened to Jonah's message—because he had been in a "great fish."

When Jonah arrives in Nineveh, the city is dark and gloomy, but not wanting to scare younger kids, the artists wanted to add some sense of comedy to it. So they made the Ninevites "fish slappers." Michael Spooner added to this drama by putting Nineveh in a deep canyon with high walls surrounding the natural space they adapted as their home. To give the city an even more foreboding feel, he designed a meteor crater in the canyon floor!

When Jonah finally arrives in Nineveh, he shares God's message and the people go through a transformation, which causes both the mood and the atmosphere to immediately change. The dark clouds, foreboding shadows, and red colors turn beautiful, helping to represent the "cleansing" of the town as the king repents.

ABOVE: Down shot of the ci▶ of Nineveh. Visual developm▶ by Michael Spooner.

LEFT: Color key of Nineveh gate by Chuck Vollmer, designed by Michael Spoo▶ and Daniel López Muñoz.

OPPOSITE: Color key of Jona▶ overlooking Nineveh by Brad Hicks.

LEFT: Visual development of pirate ship by Joseph Sapulich.

BELOW: Visual development of ship's deck by Joseph Sapulich.

RIGHT: Color key of ship's deck by Brad Hicks.

OVERLEAF: Visual development of ship's interior hold by Joseph Sapulich.

Instead of obeying God and going to Nineveh, Jonah decides to do the exact opposite. He looks on a map to find the farthest place he can run to and then hires The Pirates Who Don't Do Anything to take him there.

Creating the ship that would take Jonah on his journey out to sea required plenty of research. Since this was the ship of The Pirates Who Don't do Anything, the decision was made to give them a classic Spanish galleon, in sharp contrast to the other more historically "accurate" ships in the port of Joppa.

Another challenge of the film was to create the interior of the big fish. This is where Jonah would spend three days thinking about what he had done and asking God for a second chance. Art Director Joseph Sapulich points out that, "The entire set design is based on the Hebrew word, *Sheole*. He went to the belly of Sheole, which means 'graveyard.'" To create a graveyard feel, Joe placed ships' masts in the background that resemble tombstones and crosses.

Researching the belly of the whale required extraordinary effort. Artists spent hours in their local seafood markets sticking their heads inside various fish, just to see what it looked like. They still haven't gotten rid of the smell.

ABOVE: Concept of Jonah in the whale by Tom Bancroft.

LEFT: Khalil finds his traveling buddy. Storyboard art by Luis Contreras.

OPPOSITE: Color key of Jonah in the belly of the whale by Brad Hicks.

The road of an animated film from start to finish is a tremendous journey all its own. It takes a multitude of talented people to bring it together before the final moment of truth—the day the movie opens.

Every great movie needs a terrific story, and the story of Jonah is about a prophet who gets a message from the Lord that he doesn't want to hear. Jonah was known throughout the land. When he spoke, people listened.

The story is written and directed by both Phil and Mike, who establish Jonah's character as "the guy people can count on." But when he's told by God to go to Nineveh, a place where people don't know right from wrong, he runs in the opposite direction.

The story was developed using everyone's favorite characters from *VeggieTales*, along with an interesting new character named Khalil. "The story of Jonah is probably the only story in the Bible where a major plot point revolves around a worm," explains Phil. In the biblical account, a worm shows up near the end of the story to play a pivotal role. As he reread the story in the Bible, Phil wondered what the film would be like if the worm had actually been traveling with Jonah all along? What if he was Jonah's "traveling buddy?" So early in the film, Jonah bumps into Khalil, a very outgoing, *very* talkative Persian rug salesman who just happens to be a worm! "He is what will make this movie very entertaining," adds Michael Spooner.

Regarding the story, Art Director Joseph Sapulich, explains, "The most important part of the movie is the message. You can have pretty colors, wonderful sets, and great costumes; but it's the story that really changes lives."

Of course, it wouldn't be a Big Idea film if it didn't find a way to teach a biblical lesson or value. So when Phil and Mike first talked about tackling the story of Jonah, they had to first figure out the real lesson. Even though Phil had been raised hearing the story used over and over again to teach obedience, he and Mike quickly realized that the more profound lessons of the story were about compassion and mercy. Phil summed it up by saying, "The true central message of the film is that God wants to give *everyone* a second chance; all they have to do is *ask*."

PREVIOUS SPREAD: Visual development of Jonah in the belly of the whale by Joseph Sapulich.

OPPOSITE: Khalil gets fed-up with Jonah. Storyboard art by Tod Carter; production still.

OVERLEAF: Visual development of the choir in the belly of the whale by Joseph Sapulich.

ABOVE: Inside the whale, Jonah is taught that our God is a God of second chances. Storyboard art by Luis Contreras.

Some of the most important elements of the journey help to create a believable story and make it all come together. "We've always had a lot of fun with music in the past; so with *Jonah*, our first movie, we're kicking everything up a notch!" Phil explained after a recording session with the gospel group Anointed. The popular group sings the movie's show-stopping tune, "Second Chances." (Picture the Brooklyn Tabernacle Choir in a whale.)

"We love to combine great story telling, wacky characters, and memorable music in all our shows," says Kurt Heinecke, Music Director for *Jonah*. He plans to deliver all that fans will expect—and more—in Big Idea's first movie. David Mullen and Kurt Heinecke both worked with Phil and Mike to write and arrange the songs for the movie. "The music helps to tell the story and engages people throughout...and we end big!" says Nawrocki.

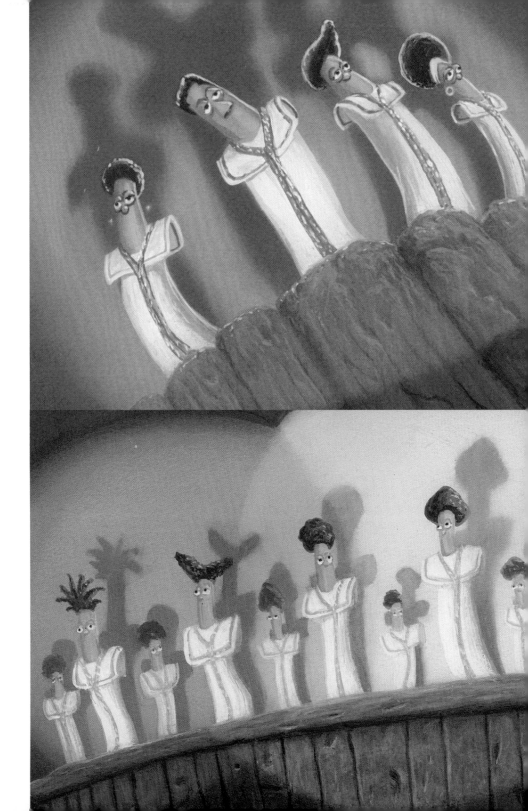

Lighting and special effects help to set the mood, affecting everything in the film that moves, other than the characters themselves. Things like wind, rain, and the roar of thunder create the dramatic storm; "and the music will have you dancing in your seats," explains Producer Ameake Owens.

Music can be used to enhance a story or put an exclamation point at the end. The music in *Jonah* heightens the drama, underscores the tension, and even makes the jokes funnier!

In addition, sound effects help to breathe life into every scene, creating a world that is much more believable and realistic. Big Idea's directors and post-production artists put so much work into the sound effects that you could almost follow the story with your eyes closed!

LEFT: Color keys of choir by Brad Hicks, designed by Joseph Sapulich.

INSET: Clothesline sequence. Storyboard art by Tim Hodge.

RIGHT: Color keys of the pirate ship in the storm by Brad Hicks.

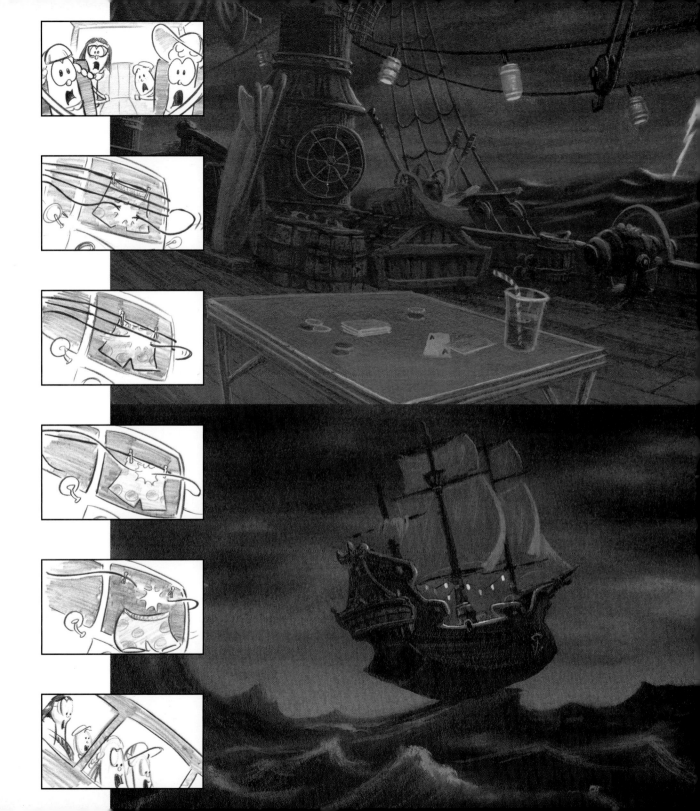

Dan Phillips, Vice President of Production, has an often-used quote that the entire Big Idea team endorses: "You never really finish; you just run out of time!" The artists at Big Idea will go on "tweaking" and improving the film until the very last minute to make it absolutely as entertaining as they can.

Almost one hundred dedicated artists have worked on the thousands of drawings, hundreds of props and models, miles of computer cable, 180 computer CPU's calculating twenty-four hours a day, using two terabytes of hard disk space over a period of $2^1/_2$ years...all to bring an eighty-eight-page script to the screen. When asked if the monumental task of making *Jonah* was worth it, Phil just smiles and says, "When we finally get to sit down in a movie theater and watch it on the big screen with our families—knowing that you'll be doing the same—we'll know that we've created an amazing new way for parents to share biblical values with their kids. That's what Big Idea has always been committed to—on small screens in your living room and now on the big screen."

That's a Big Idea!

ABOVE, RIGHT AND OPPOSITE:
The development of a scene from storyboard to visual development and finally to the image you see on screen. Storyboard art by Tim Hodge; color key by Brad Hicks, designed by Joseph Sapulich; production still.

The road through the woods was dark and lonely. The only sounds to be heard were the distant clang of a guitar mingled with an engine trudging through the valley. Then the strumming stopped, and Dad Asparagus said, "Okay, kids! Let's sing a little song about Billy Joe McGuffrey!"

The kids shouted their approval, and the song began.

Now Billy Joe McGuffrey was a really clumsy kid. On the first day of first grade, I'll tell you what he did. He tripped over a pencil box and flew up in the air! Landed on a kangaroo who pulled out all his hair!

The car chugged along, the kids sang, and all the while, Bob the Tomato fumbled with the map as they made their way to the much-anticipated Twippo concert.

Laura gazed down at the special ticket she won in the Twippo Sweepstakes. "I get to meet Twippo!" she said, anticipating the moment. "And *I'm* the only one who gets to meet him because *I* won the Twippo Sweepstakes!" she added, waving her special ticket right in Junior's face.

"Ya don't have it rub it in," Junior scowled.

"It's great that you won the contest, Laura, but let's try not to brag about it, okay?" Dad Asparagus told her.

"Maybe you could help me with the *map*!" Bob grumbled as he struggled to see where they were going.

"Oh, I'm sorry," Dad Asparagus said, quickly, noting the lack of humor in his friend's voice. He leaned over to help with the map as the van swerved and the tires began to squeal.

"Is there anything you want me to tell Twippo when I meet him?" Laura teased Junior, waving her ticket again.

Suddenly, the van veered dangerously toward the other side of the road, and Laura lost her balance. As she fell against the side of the van, her special ticket escaped her grip and flew right out the window into the night air.

"My ticket!" she screamed.

"Quick, get it!" Dad called as he turned around in his seat, whacking Bob with the neck of his guitar.

Suddenly, the van was out of control! Everyone was yelling and screaming. But no one saw the family of porcupines up ahead.

Momma Porcupine was crossing the road with her babies. She turned her head toward the van, shocked and horrified to see it tumbling toward her family. Her poor little babies, unaware of the danger soon to be upon them, looked up to her for direction.

Bob struggled to push the map below his eyes so that he could see out the window. He was just in time to catch a glimpse of Momma Porcupine turning her back toward the van to pitch a swarm of quills at the front tires of his car.

The tires exploded with a *pop-Pop-POP!*

"Aaaahhhh!" everyone yelled.

The van twisted and turned, bounced and bumped, circled and spun, as Bob tried desperately to regain control. The porcupines watched with great interest as the clattering of the van and the boisterous shouts swirled off the road and down the hill.

"Tree!" shouted Dad as they bounced through some brush.

Veering to one side, Bob avoided hitting a huge tree straight in their path.

"Cabin!" Dad yelled, as they lurched toward a tiny building in their path. Again, Bob managed to swing out of the way.

But this time they were headed right toward a gigantic clothesline strung with all sorts of clothes and one great big pair of red polka-dotted underwear! There was no way Bob could avoid this!

The kids screamed as individual shirts, pants, socks, and the great big pair of underwear plastered themselves across the windshield. Then it was suddenly quiet. Amazingly, the nylon cords held tight and had slowed the van to a stop.

"Well, I'm sure glad that's over!" Bob said at last.

P-o-i-n-g!

"Did you say something?" Dad asked nervously.

P-o-i-n-g! P-o-i-n-g! Each of the tiny cords of the clothesline snapped as the van tugged on them while lurching toward the river.

"Aaaaaaahhhhhh!" everyone shouted.

The van rolled perilously downhill as Bob, Dad, and the kids braced themselves for a wet landing. But suddenly the van stopped with a big *THUD*. An old tree stump saved them from rolling into the river.

"Phew!" the kids sighed.

"Well, at least nobody got hurt!" Bob said, as they all climbed out of the van.

D-o-i-n-k!

Everyone turned. Flying through the air was one last quill.

Bob looked over his shoulder just in time to see a small prickly plume implant itself right into his behind.

"Wow! What a shot!" Dad said with admiration as Bob groaned.

"Hey! What's that?" Junior asked, pointing to an old run-down shack under a bridge along the bank of the river.

A red neon sign buzzed and glowed, *SEAFOO*. The lights from the little building glowed eerily, dimly lighting the surrounding landscape and the tiny dock attached to one side. Fog rose from the river that overflowed onto the land.

"What's seafoo?" Annie asked, adjusting her glasses for a better look.

"Maybe it's like tofu," Percy suggested.

"Only saltier," offered Dad, as the letter *D* at the end of the sign flickered to life.

"Ooohhh! Seafood!" exclaimed Annie.

As the group made their way inside the building, Junior teased Laura about losing her special ticket and Bob scolded Dad Asparagus about not helping with the map.

"If it wasn't for you, we wouldn't be in this mess!" Bob growled.

"I said I was sorry. I'll do better next time!" Dad Asparagus repeated.

"There isn't gonna be a next time!" Bob fumed, turning to glare at the quill still stuck into his backside.

"Even if we make it to the concert, I can't get in! I lost my ticket!" Laura complained.

"Serves you right! It's your own fault for waving it in my face!" Junior reminded her.

"Where's the phone?" Bob groaned.

"Ahem! Can we help you?" the maître d' asked, making himself known when the commotion had settled.

Everyone stopped, looked at their hosts, and then each began shouting his or her own version of the story.

"One at a time!" Jean-Claude insisted.

After all their cases had been stated, Jean-Claude offered to seat them, but first the waiter paused to ask Bob, "Do you prefer 'poking' or 'non-poking'?"

"*Non!*" Bob sputtered with a forced laugh as everyone stared at the quill still stuck into his behind.

Phillipe gave a quick yank on Bob's quill to pull it out. "Viola! A skewer for zee scampi!"

The peas led the way through the mysterious seafood restaurant. The walls were festooned with sea creatures, fish nets, and photographs. An eerie light illuminated the dining area, and an unusual song could be heard from the back of the room

"We are The Pirates Who Don't Do Anything! We just stay home and lie around! And if you ask us to do anything, we'll just tell you...we don't do anything!" The catchy chorus came wafting through the room from a group of pirates who were delighted to be doing nothing in a nearby booth.

"Why don't you two wait here. I'm gonna call a tow truck. Maybe we can still make it to the concert on time," Bob said with a frown as he hopped down the hall.

Laura trailed behind, still whimpering about the loss of her ticket. Junior looked around as he sat in the booth, gloating. Suddenly, everything looked just a little bit eerie. Was that the silhouette of *pirates* in the next booth? Feeling very alone, Junior looked down at his menu and began to read.

STEAK AND SHRIMP $10.00
SCAMPI ON A SKEWER $7.50
SCAMPI ON A CLEAN SKEWER $10.00
COMPASSION . . . . .MARKET PRICE

What? Junior wondered. The last item on the menu seemed just a little bit odd to him. As he raised an eyebrow of suspicion, his thoughts were interrupted.

It was a bright and sunny day at the marketplace in Joppa. The Pirates Who Don't Do Anything had wandered into town to buy some cheese curls and root beer. Not only did they love cheese curls, but they *really* wanted to win the Mr. Twisty's Cheese Curl Sweepstakes. But Mr. Nezzer refused to sell to the pirates because they had not paid him what they already owed him.

As the pirates turned to leave, they saw the prophet Jonah riding into town on his camel, Reginald. He smiled pleasantly to the passersby as he made his way down the road, noting that everyone was quite pleased to see him.

Prophets were people that God used to deliver very special messages to Israel. They were a little like mailmen, except their letters came straight from God!

"What's the word, Jonah?" shouted Mr. Nezzer and the people of Israel. Everyone was anxious to hear if God had spoken to Jonah recently.

Jonah hopped down off his camel and addressed the crowd that had gathered. "Dear people, I bring you a message from the Lord!"

"Excuse me!" a pirate called over the side of the booth.

Startled, Junior dropped his menu and gazed up at three pirates who were staring at him.

"Who are you?" Junior asked.

"We're The Pirates Who Don't Do Anything," explained Pa Grape.

"Zilch," added Mr. Lunt.

"Nada," added Larry.

"We couldn't help but notice you were havin' a little thing with your friend over there," the pirate explained.

"Yeah. You weren't being very nice," Mr. Lunt chimed in.

"Well, it's her own fault! She was teasing me, and now she's getting what she deserves!" Junior explained.

"What you need is a little compassion," Pa Grape went on.

"Hey! I saw that in the menu! What is that? What's compassion?" Junior asked.

"Well, compassion is when ya see that someone needs help and ya wanna help 'em!" Pa Grape tried to explain. "We find it helpful to illustrate with a little story."

It would be the most remarkable story Junior might ever hear. Pa Grape cleared his throat and this is the story he told.

There were gasps, sighs, and much anticipation as the people gathered to hear what Jonah would say next. And Jonah was so delighted by his warm reception that he broke into a song.

Do not fight, do not cheat, wash your hands before you eat. There is nothing quite as sweet as a message from the Lord! Be a friend, say your prayers. Heaven loves a heart that cares. That is why I've come to share a message from the Lord!

Before long, Jonah had the entire town singing with him as he and Reginald told the people of Joppa about God's message.

"Alright, everyone! Thank you very much!" Jonah cried out to the people as they finished the song, and he turned to leave. The life of a prophet in Israel was very prestigious...until a prophet received a message that he didn't really want to hear—or tell—at all!

It had been a long tiring day, and Jonah was worn out. But every night, before Jonah went to sleep, he would pray and ask God if there was a new message for him to deliver. This night, there was a message that would change Jonah's life.

"What? Go to Nineveh?" Jonah asked, certain he must have been mistaken. So he opened his eyes and scanned the map hanging on the wall of his tent. "I'm not aware of any Nineveh in Israel," he told the Lord.

"Oh, you mean *that* Nineveh?" Jonah shrieked. *That* Nineveh wasn't in Israel at all! It was the capital of Assyria, and it was the biggest, meanest city around! In fact, the people in Nineveh were particularly mean to Jonah's people, the Israelites. They lied! They stole! But worst of all, they slapped people with fishes! They didn't know the difference between right and wrong.

The Ninevites were so mean, in fact, that most of the Israelites, including Jonah, wished God would just wipe Nineveh off the face of the Earth!

"You don't want me to go *there*! You don't know what *Nineveh* is like! Perhaps you've never been there! Well, of course you haven't! A God like you would never go to a place like *Nineveh*! For that matter, neither would a prophet like me!" Jonah said, getting quite haughty about the whole, preposterous idea!

With that, Jonah ripped off the section of the map that contained the land of Nineveh, crumpled it up, and tossed it right out of his tent.

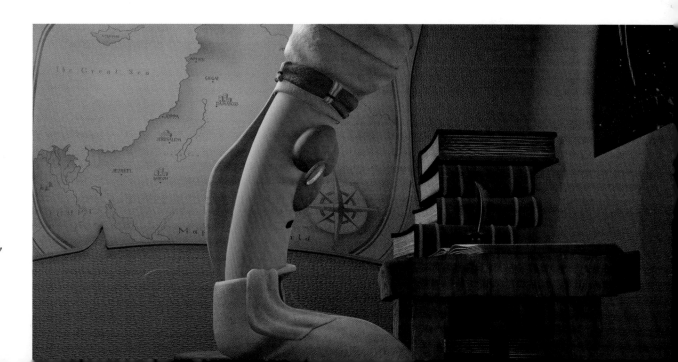

"Yup. It sounded like God wanted to offer mercy to the Ninevites," Pa Grape explained to Junior as Bob returned to the booth.

Bob explained that the tow truck was on its way. That's when Mr. Lunt encouraged *him* to listen to the story too.

"What's mercy?" Laura asked. This was a new word for her!

"It's what this whole story is about," Mr. Lunt told her.

"Check your menu again. We have got *two* specials today, and they go hand in hand!" Pa Grape declared, looking toward the menu on the table.

Sure enough, Junior picked up the menu and saw, "MERCY... MARKET PRICE" right beneath the word COMPASSION.

"Compassion is when you want to help someone who needs help. Mercy is when you give someone a second chance, even if they don't deserve it!" Larry explained. "This story is about both of them!"

"So what did Jonah do?" Laura asked.

Never before had Jonah gotten a message from God that he didn't want to deliver. He didn't know what to do. So he tried to slip out of his tent, hoping to avoid the people of Israel. But everywhere he went, people were anxious to hear about the next message from God.

"There is no word! I have no message!" Jonah lied, trying to escape the eager questions of those around him.

Before long, Jonah found himself staring at a map near a small booth beside a dock at sea. The booth sold tickets for cruises to many different places, and Jonah was anxious to go anywhere...other than Nineveh.

"What's the farthest thing in the world from Nineveh?" Jonah stuttered, looking at the map. His eyes scanned the chart and came to rest at the outermost spot he could find. "There! I want to go there!" he said, pointing to a place called Tarshish.

But no one else wanted to go *that* far, and no one was willing to sell him a ticket to get there. That's when Jonah saw the pirates. They were just lounging around and listening to music, apparently not doing anything!

"We couldn't possibly! We're very busy... with... cargo... and stuff." Pa Grape said in a very flustered way when he saw Jonah looking at them.

"You know, pirates have to pillage and plunder and... uh, that really takes it out of you!" griped Mr. Lunt.

"And besides that, we don't really sail... at all," said Pa Grape.

Jonah paused and thought. Then he looked at the three Pirates Who Don't Do Anything and said, "Money is no object."

There was an awkward pause. The pirates looked at one another and then at Jonah.

"Next stop, Tarshish! I'll hoist the mainsail!" Pa Grape called out.

"I'll pop the popcorn!" Larry chimed in.

"I'll get the moist towelettes!" Mr. Lunt added.

The pirates scurried around in every direction, thrilled at the prospect of making so much money that they would never want for cheese curls again!

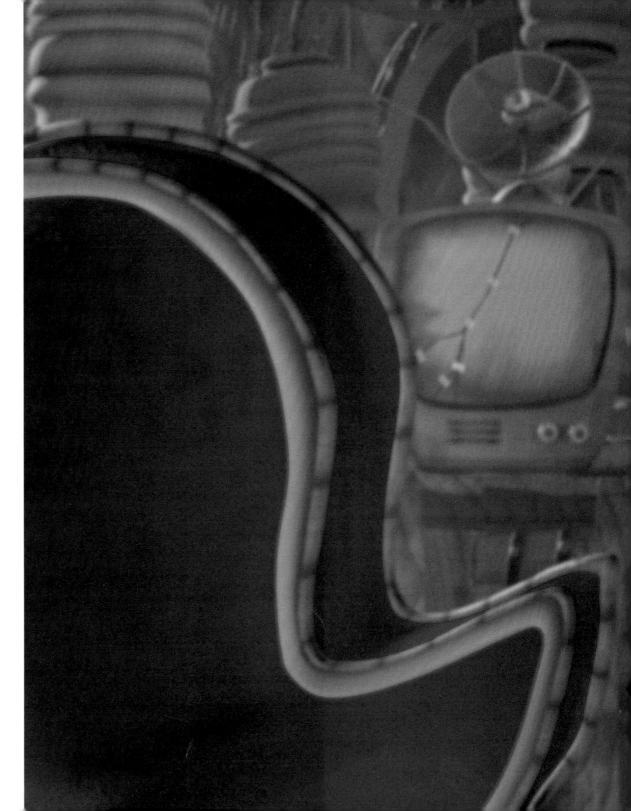

"Oh, what have I done?" Jonah moaned down in the ship's hold as he leaned against a bag of Mr. Twisty's Twisted Cheese Curls. He was startled by an odd voice.

"Oww! What did you do that for?" asked a strange-looking, very irritated worm who crawled out of the bag.

"What are you?" Jonah asked, uncertain what this creature was.

"My name is Khalil. I am a caterpillar. Well, that's only half true. My mother was a caterpillar. My father was a worm. But I'm okay with that now," Khalil explained as he dusted himself off. "By the way, do you know where this ship is going?"

"Um… Tarshish," Jonah replied. "Now if you don't mind, Carlyle, I think I'll just get some rest."

"Jonah?" Khalil shouted, suddenly recognizing him. "The most famous prophet in the whole world?" he said, with great praise and adoration.

Jonah tried to suppress a smile that was just begging to escape. "Well, I don't know if I'd say…"

"You go from town to town delivering God's messages! You are a big shot!" Khalil continued. "A man God can *count* on to deliver his messages!"

Jonah's smile faded away. Why did the worm have to bring *that* up at a time like this?

"You and God are like two peas in a pod! Like two humps on a camel. You always sway the same way!" Khalil went on gleefully.

Jonah's spirits fell deeper and lower than ever before. This little worm was not helping him forget why he was headed to Tarshish.

"Oh, that's a good one!" Khalil laughed, "You know, humor runs very deep in my family! My uncle was a big star back at a comedy club in Nineveh... the Taj Ma-Haha. Standing room only," he added. "Then he was hit with a fish. I'm telling you, those people don't know right from wrong!"

"Please, Carlyle... I just need to get some rest," Jonah pleaded.

"It's Khalil. But you can call me Carlyle, if you want to. When we get to Tarshish, you can deliver the message, and I'll sell plush toys. We can be a team!" Khalil said, beaming at the idea.

But Jonah was not impressed. He just groaned and turned away from the worm.

"Well, sweet dreams, traveling buddy!" Khalil said.

"Jonah! Jonah!" Pa Grape said, shaking Jonah who had been tossing about in his bunk.

Jonah awoke with a pirate hovering over him and water splashing in his face from the rocking boat. There was water everywhere!

"What? What's happening?" Jonah asked, feeling rather groggy

"We seem to have sprung a leak, traveling buddy," Khalil explained, as he floated by on top of a barrel.

"How can you sleep at a time like this? We're all gonna be fish food if I don't get some help!" Pa Grape exclaimed. "We're in a storm like I've never seen before! If we don't do something quick, we're gonna sink!"

"Well, what can we do?" Jonah asked eagerly.

"Get up and pray to your God! Maybe he'll have mercy on us and spare our lives. Oy!" Pa Grape muttered as he turned and hopped back toward the deck. "Somebody up there must be really upset with somebody down here!"

Back on deck, the thunder crashed and the lightning crackled as the waves rose higher and higher!

"Alright ya lazies," Pa Grape barked at Larry and Mr. Lunt who were playing Go Fish. "Shuffle 'em up and deal us in."

Everyone gathered together at the table as Mr. Lunt shuffled the cards.

"Here's the deal. Somebody up there is *really* upset with somebody down here. And it's not gonna let up until we know who that somebody is," Pa Grape explained as everyone began looking at one another with great suspicion.

"All right everyone...go fish! Loser takes a swim!" Pa Grape ordered as lightning flashed in the sky.

Then the game began. The cards were dealt. Pairs were made. Each player took turns having to go fish, and each had moments when it looked as if he might win. While they played, the storm persisted. The thunder grew louder. The waves rose higher. And each player wondered who would take a swim!

Finally, there were only two players remaining. Khalil nervously looked at Jonah and said, "You got any...trout?"

Jonah's face said it all. He slid Khalil the card he wanted. Then Khalil laid them down and was out! Jonah had lost the game.

"Alright! I admit it!" Jonah confessed. "It's all *my* fault! *I'm* the one to blame!"

Khalil looked at his new traveling buddy. How could this be? How could Jonah, the great prophet, be at fault for this storm?

"I worship the Lord, the God of heaven, who made the sea and the land. And I'm running away from him! He told me to go to Nineveh, but I didn't listen. You know, I don't *like* those people," Jonah cried with a nasty scowl on his face.

"Ooooh. Fish slappers," Mr. Lunt chimed in, with great understanding.

"So I ran and I ended up here, and now everyone's in terrible danger all because of me. I'm afraid the only thing I can do is throw myself into the sea! Then it shall become calm again," Jonah proclaimed.

"Awww...you don't have to do that! We got a plank. You can just walk off!" Larry assured him.

"Yes, thank you. You're too kind," Jonah managed.

The storm continued to toss the ship frantically about as Jonah stood at the edge of the plank wearing a small rubber ducky flotation ring and a swim cap that Larry had offered him. The pirates stood nearby with their heads bowed and their eyes closed.

"Oh Lord, don't let us die for this man's sin. And don't hold us responsible for his death, because it isn't our fault," the pirates prayed.

"And keep my ducky safe," Larry added with emphasis.

"Amen," the pirates concluded.

Jonah took one last look at the pirates and turned back toward the sea. Khalil inched forward from a bowling ball he was hiding in to get one final look at his traveling buddy before he took the big plunge.

Jonah bounced once. Then Jonah bounced twice. Then finally, Jonah bounced right off the plank and into the sea! All at once, the sea became calm. The clouds parted, and the sun came out. It was a beautiful day.

Jonah bobbed up and down softly in the water, hugged by his little ducky ring. He was quite amazed at the sudden turn in the weather.

"That was easy," Pa Grape said, not seeing the swirling waters encircling Jonah.

Then Jonah felt something brush up against him in the water. Looking around nervously, Jonah's heart began to flutter. Even the pirates noticed that something didn't seem quite right. So they quickly tossed a life ring out to him but missed miserably.

"Something touched mc!" Jonah yelped, getting more and more nervous as he bobbed up and down in the water.

Each pirate frantically took turns tossing the life ring out to Jonah as the waters continued to churn. Then Jonah got a sudden push right toward the ring.

"Please hurry!" Jonah shrieked. "There's something in the water!"

The pirates began yelling frantically as Larry tried once more to toss the ring out to Jonah, and this time it landed right over him. He smiled proudly as everyone sighed with relief and began tugging Jonah back toward the boat.

Suddenly, a gigantic and most extraordinary whale leapt right out of the water and swallowed Jonah whole!

The pirates' eyes grew enormous. They couldn't believe what they'd seen!

"Ooops," said Larry, looking to his friends for help.

Then the rope was pulled straight out from the boat and snapped taut. They had become attached to the whale too! As the ship raced through the water, the pirates scrambled about helplessly.

"Man the cannon!" Pa Grape commanded.

"Aye, aye, Cap'n!" Mr. Lunt replied. But after he looked around, he shouted, "We don't got no ammo!"

"Oh yes we do!" Larry offered, quickly gathering the leisure gear The Pirates Who Don't Do Anything had grown so fond of. Stuffing a tennis racket into the cannon, Larry prepared to save the day as the ship zipped through the water.

"Fire one!" Pa Grape yelled above the roar of the waves.

Mr. Lunt pulled the string on the cannon, and the tennis racket flew through the air. It splashed into the sea, far away from the whale.

"Fire Two!"

This time two croquet mallets flew through the air but with the same result as the tennis racket. Spotting the Art Bigotti bowling-ball bag, Larry bounced over to the jackpot-of-all ammunition.

Stuffed into the cannon along with the bowling ball, Khalil poked his head out and looked around. "Is this part of the cruise package?" he asked shakily.

"Fire three!" Pa Grape commanded as the string was pulled and the ball roared into the air.

The pirates followed the ball's flight and listened as Khalil screamed, "I'm coming traveling buddy!" Then he gave a little whistle. "Traveling buddy? Where are you?"

The whale leapt into the air and caught the bowling ball with one big gulp as the pirates looked on in astonishment. Crashing back into the water, the whale once again disappeared below the sea.

"That boy really knows how to go fish," Pa Grape said as the little ducky flotation ring popped out of the water with the life ring.

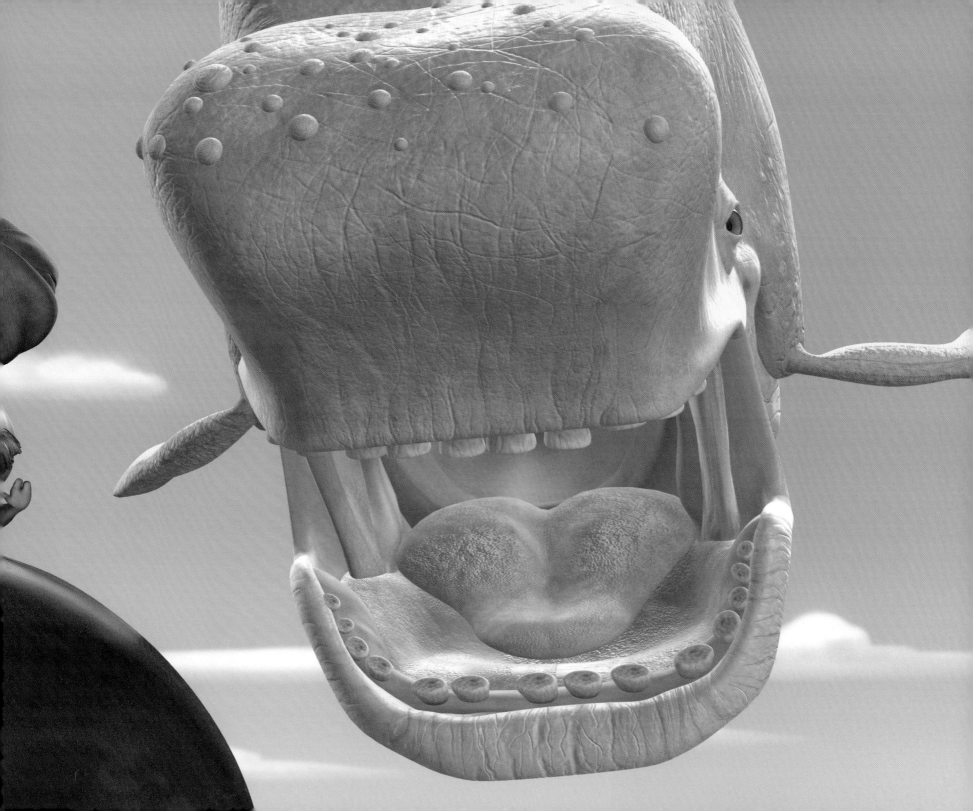

"Oh look, a bowling ball," said Jonah as the ball rolled up next to him inside the whale. Jonah sat on a barrel inside the dark, hollow fish, looking quite forlorn. "If only I could find some bowling pins..."

"You found better than that, traveling buddy! It's me!" Khalil said, bursting out of the ball with a big smile on his face. "Forget about Tarshish! All we need to do is get this whale to swim to Nineveh!" Khalil explained. "You give the message; I sell the plush toys. We'll be right back on track."

"Carlyle, please don't speak to me. I'm having a rather bad day," Jonah pleaded.

"Well, you don't need to be so down about it, Mr. Grumpy-pants!" Khalil pouted.

"Look around you! We're inside a whale!" Jonah shouted, startled by the echo that bounced back at him. "We're going to be *digested*! Do you know what that means?"

"Of course I do. Digestion runs very deep in my family. I'm just trying to have a positive outlook, you know," Khalil said. "You know the difference between you and me is that you see the whale as half empty, but I see the whale as half full!"

"I might as well face it. God gave me a job to do, and I disobeyed him. Now I'm getting what I deserve. I'm going to die here in this whale," Jonah moaned.

Khalil looked at his friend. How could he possibly cheer him up? Everything Jonah said was true. But while Khalil pondered what to do, he thought he heard voices.

"Have you ever seen anything so pathetic?"

"Mmm mmm. This boy needs some help!"

"What? Who's there?" Jonah called out, hearing the voices, too.

"Take it easy, Jonah! We're on your side!"

"How do you know my name? How did you get in here?" Jonah asked a woman standing amidst an entire group of...

what were they anyway? Messengers of some sort?

"Were *you* in the bowling ball, too?" Khalil wondered aloud.

"Oh, no. That's not how we get around. We came straight from the Big Man himself! And just like you, we deliver his messages!"

"So you're prophets too?" Jonah asked, pleased to be in the company of others who were just like him.

"Not exactly. Ya see, we work on a slightly *higher* level," they explained.

"And Jonah, we've got a message for you!" said another one, before the entire group broke into song!

You're feelin' pretty blue, you didn't do what God requested. Yeah, I'd be mopin' too, if I was gonna be digested! This ain't a pretty picture, no! It ain't a pretty sight. You ran from God this morning, and you're whale chow tonight!

Praise the Lord! He's the God of second chances! You'll be floored! How his love your life enhances! You can be restored from the darkest circumstances. Our God is the God of second chances!

Everyone sat with rapt attention; anxiously waiting to hear the pirates tell what happened next.

"So from inside the whale, Jonah prayed and asked God to forgive him for not obeying. He told God that if he got another chance, he would go to Nineveh, even though he didn't like those people very much," Pa Grape explained.

"So did he get another chance?" Bob asked, eager to know the outcome.

Pa Grape smiled slyly, knowing the answer. "Shouldn't you be lookin' out for yer tow truck?"

"Yeah, yeah, yeah. That can wait. Did Jonah get another chance?" Bob asked again.

"Well, God saw that Jonah needed help, and he wanted to help him," Pa Grape said, keeping each of his listeners on the very edge of their seats.

"That's compassion!" Junior said, recognizing the explanation he had been given before the story began.

"But did he give him a second chance, even though he didn't deserve it?" Bob wanted to know. "You know...mercy?"

"After three days, something strange began to happen..." Pa Grape said, continuing with the rest of the story.

Jonah and Khalil noticed the belly of the whale begin to rumble. Then the whale burped, and Jonah shot through the air like a bullet, sailing into the sky with Khalil holding tight to his bag. They careened across the waters until they landed in a heap on the sandy beach.

Jonah looked around, a little dazed. He was quite pale, and his clothes were tattered and wrapped with seaweed.

"Ohhh!" he moaned loudly as he looked right up into the face of his trusted friend, Reginald.

The camel looked down at Jonah fondly and waited for him to get up.

"Reginald! Good to see you!" Jonah exclaimed, most delighted to see a familiar face. Then he prepared himself to continue on to Nineveh.

It was a long ride to Nineveh. The countryside was barren and deserted. The clip-clop, clip-clop of Reginald's hooves seemed to echo as Jonah and Khalil strode underneath the afternoon sun toward a land of people that Jonah was not too anxious to meet.

Jonah was terribly nervous as he approached the dark and foreboding city. He'd heard terrible things could happen to strangers who showed up in Nineveh!

But just as Jonah had promised, he and Khalil arrived in the city of Nineveh. The sky was cloudy and gray. They passed a sign that said Welcome to Nineveh—Home of Mister Twisty's Twisted Cheese Curls, followed by another sign that said Visitors Welcome—To Leave! Sounds of people slapping one another with fishes smacked through the air!

Jonah swallowed hard as he looked around and remembered the message God wanted him to share. This was certainly not going to be easy!

Then a man came running right toward him! His eyes were opened wide with terror and fright, and he was screaming, "Turn back! Turn back!"

Jonah and Khalil looked at each other, clearly frightened. Nonetheless, they forged bravely ahead. As they approached the gates to the city, two guards stepped out to block their path.

"Who goes 'ere?" said the guard with a rather strange accent.

"Ah, yes...my name is Jonah...and I'm a prophet from..." Jonah tried to answer before he was interrupted.

"You're not from 'ere, are you?"

"Um...no. You see, I'm from..."

"That would make you a *stranger*, wouldn't it?" the guard barked angrily.

"Well, um, yes. I suppose so," Jonah concurred.

"We don't like strangers!" snapped the second guard. "So why are you 'ere?"

"Well, I have a message...for everyone...in the whole city!" Jonah explained.

"Oh!" laughed the guard. "Well, I'll alert the king! Your honor! A bleached asparagus has a message for us all!" the guard mocked as he and the other guard laughed hysterically at Jonah's proclamation.

"I do not think this is going very well," Khalil whispered to his friend.

"Well, I tried!" Jonah sighed, having concluded that he had done his best.

"I tried to deliver the message, but it didn't work out. Oh well. Maybe next time." With that, Jonah turned Reginald around and began to leave the city. But he didn't get far. Only a few moments later, he heard someone call his name.

"Jonah?" came a familiar voice.

Jonah spun around to see The Pirates Who Don't Do Anything standing in the entrance of the city, apparently on their way out. They were each wearing a hat with what appeared to be a giant cheeze curl on their head. Jonah stared in disbelief.

The pirates were equally bewildered, as they could not believe that Jonah had survived being digested by the giant fish!

"It looks like him," Mr. Lunt said through squinty eyes.

"But it couldn't be him. Cuz he's..." Larry mumbled.

"Fish food!" Pa Grape finished for him.

Khalil was delighted and immediately exclaimed, "It's our friends from the ship!"

The pirates hurried over to see the miracle that had taken place.

"Yes! It *was* a miracle," Jonah told them. "We were in the whale for three days. And then I prayed for a second chance, and well, God gave us one!"

The pirates marveled at what had happened as Jonah and Khalil told their story.

"But the Ninevites won't let us into their city, so we're going home. Such is life!" Jonah concluded as he readied himself to journey back home.

"Hey!" cried Mr. Lunt. "I bet we could get him in..."

Jonah was a bit stunned. He did not expect this! Khalil, however, was quite pleased.

The Pirates Who Don't Do Anything led the way back to the city gates. Sure enough, the guards immediately recognized them and welcomed them back. The pirates explained that Jonah and Khalil were with them, as Jonah begrudgingly went along.

"Alright. You can come in," said the guard still looking at jonah with great suspicion.

"What was all that about? How did you do that?" Jonah questioned.

The pirates explained that they had used the money Jonah had given them to buy cheese curls.

"And you'll never guess what we found in bag number 497." Larry said.

Jonah didn't have a clue.

"The golden ticket!" Pa said, filling him in. "We won the Mister Twisty's Twisted Cheese Curl Sweepstakes!"

"Oh," Jonah remarked flatly as he stared at their hats. "And the prize was...?"

"Yep!" Pa said with a smile, as he noted Jonah's fascination with their hats. "But in addition to our enviably fashionable headgear, we also got a tour of Mister Twisty's factory—right here in Nineveh!"

The pirates went on to tell Jonah and Khalil that the entire city of Nineveh now considered them to be celebrities!

The group traveled on toward the crowded marketplace. No one looked very happy, and many of the Ninevites were slapping each other with fishes!

"Hey look! Here comes a city official to greet us!" Mr. Lunt remarked as several guards walked aggressively toward them. But they were not too happy about what happened next.

"These are the men!" the official snapped. "Arrest them at once!"

Jonah, Khalil, and the pirates were stunned. What had they done wrong? They demanded to know the charge.

"Thievery! High theft against the royal city of Nineveh!" the official told them. Then he pulled off Larry's hat and watched as bags of Mister Twisty's Cheese Curls fell to the ground.

"No! Wait! I thought they were free samples!" Larry protested.

But it was too late. The guards quickly approached, and *smack*! They were all struck with fishes.

Jonah regained consciousness as a black bag was lifted off his head. A large crowd of Ninevites was standing in a circle around him. Because they were staring at him, Jonah assumed it was time for his big speech.

A moment later, bags came off of Pa Grape and the other pirates' heads too. They all tried to move but found that they couldn't. "Hey! I can't move!" Pa Grape called out.

Jonah looked toward the pirate and what he saw made his eyes bulge and his mouth drop open.

They were all tied back to back beneath a huge metal fish held up by a rope!

"What? Have I got somethin' on my face?" the pirate asked Jonah. As Pa Grape scrutinized Jonah's reaction, he, too, noticed Jonah's predicament.

Everyone gasped.

"I'm sorry, guys!" Larry moaned on the verge of tears. "I thought they were free samples! They were right out in the open...in a big bowl. It was very misleading!"

"Oh, don't go blamin' yourself," Pa said, trying to comfort him.

"We are going to die!" Mr. Lunt groaned.

They were interrupted by a city official who announced, "People of Nineveh! These four men...and that small...whatever it is..."

"I am a caterpillar!" Khalil called out, quite annoyed. "Well, that is only half true..." he muttered to himself.

"...have been found guilty of high thievery against the royal city of Nineveh!" the official continued as the crowd hissed. "For their punishment, 'The Slap of No Return!'"

The crowd looked at the fish poles, not quite sure what they were for. This irritated the official who assumed the Ninevites had no respect for his latest invention.

"Observe!" the official snapped. Everyone looked on as the official placed a large pumpkin on a small wooden platform. Carefully sitting it in front of the fish pole, he then walked over to a rope that was anchored to a stake in the ground. Raising his sword high in the air, he brought it down with a big SWOOSH! and the rope was severed. The fish fell and splattered the pumpkin into pulp.

The pumpkin bits splattered onto Jonah, and the crowd cheered. Jonah and the pirates were horrified and burst into a panic of tears and blubbering.

"What is happening that is making you all cry like little babies?" Khalil asked, unable to see anything.

"Why on earth do you people take snack food so *seriously*?" Jonah asked in a desperate plea to get the city to understand. But his urgent cry for help was interrupted by the fanfare of a trumpet.

"People of Nineveh! I give you King Twistomer!"

On a balcony several stories up, a large grumpy king stood before the crowd.

"It's Mister Twisty!" Pa Grape said with awe.

"He looks happier on the bag," Larry noticed.

"Your royal gourdliness," the city official began, "these are the perpetrators of the heinous act against your curls of cheese! Their punishment is 'The Slap of No Return!'"

The crowd exploded with approval as the king smiled with satisfaction. "Proceed!" he bellowed.

The city official spun with his sword as Jonah frantically began to squirm beneath his ropes. "Wait! Won't you at least give the guilty parties the chance to speak in their own defense?"

The king agreed, and Jonah explained to the king and the crowd how the snacks were right out in the open. He begged them to see how misleading this was, and just as it looked as if the king might soften, the king pronounced, "Slap them!"

Again the sword flashed high in the air as the pirates whimpered. But once again, Jonah implored them to listen.

"You don't understand!" he pleaded. "I'm not *really* with them. I mean... how could I be? While they were taking the tour, I was in the belly of a whale!"

The city official froze. The crowd hushed, and the official demanded Jonah explain himself.

"I was in the whale for three days and three nights! Then I prayed to my God, and the great monster spit me up onto the shore so that I could bring you all a message!"

The king thought about this and said, "Here in Nineveh, we bow to the great fish. We celebrate the great fish in our art! If what you are saying is true..."

"How do we know if he's telling the truth, sire?" the city official asked.

"*Smell* him!" the king declared with great authority.

The official cautiously approached Jonah and took a big whiff. He smelled *terrible*! The official staggered back, reeling from the odor as he struggled to maintain his balance.

"I'm terribly sorry," Jonah apologized. "I've been meaning to shower…"

"He has been in the great fish!" the king pronounced. "We must hear the message!"

"The message…yes…what *was* the message?" Jonah mumbled, trying to think for a moment. Khalil nudged him on. "It's been so long, I…" Jonah mumbled. "Oh yes! *Stop it!*"

The crowd gasped at Jonah's words. The king was stunned. What was he saying? What could this mean?

"Stop cheating! Stop lying! And especially, stop slapping people with fishes! Or this entire city will be destroyed!" Jonah continued quite emphatically.

The city shuddered at the thought.

"A message from the Lord!" Jonah finished, feeling very content. The Ninevites were astonished. The king was upset! He had no idea they weren't supposed to do that stuff. No one had ever told them that before! Then a decree from the king was handed down for reading.

"A decree from the king!" the official began. "Do not let any man or beast, herd or flock eat anything. Let everyone call urgently to God. Let them give up their evil ways and their violence. Who knows? The God who brought this man out of the great fish may give us a second chance!"

The crowd erupted in mass approval. They were ready to do just as the Lord had instructed. They would stop being mean. They would even stop slapping each other with fishes!

"And let the asparagus and his friends go free!" the king added.

Once Jonah and his friends were untied, the crowd congratulated them all. The king and the people said they were very sorry, and they stopped the slapping with fishes. By the next day, the clouds in the city had broken up, and the sun shone through brightly once again.

Jonah and Khalil bid the people farewell as they made their way out of town and climbed to a hilltop just outside of Nineveh.

"What are we doing?" Khalil asked curiously, wondering why they had stopped there.

"Oh, it's time to watch the fun!" Jonah answered. "I did what I was supposed to do. I warned them that they were going to get into big trouble! So now it's time to watch God wipe them off the face of the Earth!" Jonah gloated.

But Khalil did not quite understand.

"I picked a safe distance so that we won't get singed," Jonah explained. Then he sat back to watch the destruction. "This is going to be great! The bad guys are finally getting what they deserve!"

The hours passed, the sun got hotter, and Jonah began to wilt in the heat of the day. But God showed Jonah compassion once again. He caused a plant to grow that shaded him from the hot sun.

Jonah watched the large weed grow over his head like an umbrella. "Oh! Yes! Very nice! Thank you!" Then Jonah settled back in the nice shade that God had provided and continued to watch for Nineveh to be destroyed.

Khalil looked at his friend sitting in the shade. Then he looked at the weedy vine providing that shade. Suddenly, he was hungry!

"Alright! I did my job!" Jonah said, standing to remind God that perhaps he was forgetting something. "So... fire! Brimstone! Whatever! You pick! Right over there!" he added, nodding toward the city of Nineveh. "I'll just sit here under my weed...and wait."

But when Jonah sat back down to lean against the weed, he tumbled over! "How could you?" Jonah screeched, watching Khalil happily munching on his weed.

"All your whining made me hungry! And it was just a weed." Khalil answered.

"Just a weed! It was my shade! It was my friend! Oh, dear Lord, how could you let this happen?" Jonah wailed.

That was all Khalil could take. "Would you look at yourself?" he shouted. "You care more about that weed than about all the people of Nineveh! Why are you here now, instead of back in the belly of that whale?"

"Well...I..." Jonah stuttered.

"Because God is compassionate! He wanted to help you! And because he is merciful! He gave you a second chance. Has it ever occurred to you that maybe God loves *everybody*? That maybe he wants to give *everyone* a second chance! God saw that those people needed help—that they didn't know right from wrong—so he wanted to help them! That is why he sent you!" Khalil explained with much irritation. "Don't you see? *God wants to give everyone a second chance! All they have to do is ask!*"

Jonah stood there pondering what Khalil had said. For a moment, he appeared to be somewhat moved, but then he started to sulk once again and said, "Well, if those fish slappers get a second chance, then it would be better if I were dead! Oh, I wish I were back in that whale!"

Khalil could not believe his ears. "You are pathetic! You know, patience runs very deep in my family...but not *that* deep. I'm out of here!"

"What? What are you doing?" Jonah called to the worm.

"I wanted to be big and important... just like you," Khalil told him, turning back one last time.

"But the world doesn't need more people who are big and important. The world needs more people who are nice...and *compassionate*...and *merciful!* That's what I want to be. You can find yourself a new traveling buddy. Good-bye!"

"You can't just leave!" Jonah cried. "Whom will I talk to? Reginald? Hello? Carlyle? Oh, what was your name again?" Jonah called out. But it was too late. Khalil was already gone.

"The end!" said Pa Grape as he slid the divider shut between the booths.

"Wait a minute...it's over?" Bob asked the pirates.

"Yup!"

"But what did Jonah learn?" Junior asked.

Mr. Lunt slid open the divider and said, "The question, my friends, is not 'What did *Jonah* learn?' The question is, 'What did *you* learn?'"

Junior thought about that. Laura thought about that. Bob and Dad Asparagus thought about that. Even Percy and Annie thought about it. Are *you* thinking about it too?

"Hey! Tomato." Pa Grape shouted toward Bob. "Your friend there...the big asparagus. If I'm not mistaken, he didn't do such a good job helping with the map."

"Oh, it was a disaster!" Bob groaned. "He said he was sorry and he'd do better next time, but no way! Uh uh!"

Bob looked at Dad Asparagus and then turned back to face the pirates. Then he looked down. "Mercy...I guess everyone deserves a second chance."

"Hmm. I learned something today!" Bob smiled.

"Yup! Now get outa here before my crab legs get cold!" Pa Grape added.

"You know, that still wasn't a very good way to end a story!" Dad remarked, not too pleased with the way things turned out.

"Well, whadya want? A big musical number?" Pa Grape bellowed from his booth.

"Well...yeah!" Dad answered with a smile.

"Who do they think I am? Twippo?" Pa Grape asked Larry.

At that very moment, a voice could be heard from out in the lobby of the restaurant. Junior looked at Laura.

Dad Asparagus looked at Bob. Bob looked at Annie. They *knew* that voice! It was Twippo himself!

"Twippo!" everyone shouted as he entered the dining area.

The group rushed over to see why Twippo was there. He explained that he had gotten lost and needed directions. Then everyone began to share their tale of how they, too, had gotten stranded at the seafood restaurant.

"Good heavens! Well, if it's a ride you need, I've got plenty of room in my bus; you can all come with me!" Twippo told them.

Everyone cheered! Everyone...except for Laura. Junior looked at Laura and saw how sad she was. Then, remembering the story about Jonah, he decided to show some compassion and mercy too. Junior gave Laura his ticket.

"But I...Junior...It was *my* fault!" Laura protested.

"No...I *want* you to have it!" Junior insisted. It felt *good* to show Laura compassion and mercy!

Twippo was so impressed by this show of compassion and mercy that he gave them all backstage passes to the concert!

"Speaking of mercy, have any of you heard the story of a man named Jonah?" Twippo asked.

"Yes!" they all exclaimed.

"Oh, well...Would you like to hear a song about it?"

The lights in the restaurant dimmed. All eyes gazed toward the tiny stage where Twippo stood, holding his guitar.

Twippo sang as his audience bounced along and listened. But when Twippo struck the last cord on his guitar and everyone burst into applause, they were interrupted with a voice from the back of the restaurant. Everyone turned to see who it was.

"I hate to break up the party, but who needed a tow?" asked a familiar-looking worm.

"Ah...have we met?" asked Twippo.

1. How many people from the Vischer family provide voices for VeggieTales characters in the movie?

2. To get to Tarshish, who is the VeggieTales character from whom Jonah wants to buy a cruise ticket?

3. Out of what did Billy Joe McGuffrey fall when he was in third grade?

4. A picture of what famous fish is hanging on the wall of the seafood restaurant?

5. What is the favorite food of The Pirates Who Don't Do Anything?

6. What are the two games that The Pirates Who Don't Do Anything enjoy playing?

7. In what is Khalil hiding when he is shot out of the cannon? In what is he hiding when he is discovered on the ship?

8. On the ship, to what is Khalil listening when he is discovered by Jonah?

9. What is the last pair of cards to be laid out at the end of the Go Fish game?

10. What two items does Larry let Jonah borrow when he jumps off the gangplank?

11. How many veggies appear in more than one role in the movie? Who are they?

12. What is the incorrect name Jonah calls the worm, Khalil?

13. What is the number of the bag in which the pirates find the "golden ticket?"

14. What does Pa Grape want to finish eating after telling the Jonah story?

15. What road is Twippo trying to find to get to his concert?

ANSWERS: 1) Three: Phil, Lisa, and Shelby 2) Scooter 3) A fishing boat 4) Moby Dick 5) Cheese curls 6) Parcheesi and Go Fish 7a) A bowling ball 7b) A bag of Mr. Twisty's Twisted Cheese Curls 8) Self-improvement tapes 9) Trout 10) Rubber ducky floatation ring and swim cap 11) Archibald: Jonah/Twippo; Jonah/Twippo; Peas: Waiters/fish slappers; Khalil: The worm/tow truck driver 12) Carlyle 13) 497 14) Crab legs 15) Route 59